P9-EDB-062

Color and Play Instructions:

1. **Find a Color and Play page in your coloring book and color the picture.**

2. **Download the FREE Disney Color and Play App on your mobile device and follow the instructions to create a magical 3D version of your coloring masterpiece in this book!**

3. **Using the Color and Play App, hold your device over the picture until you see the ⭐ in the corners.**

Watch your picture come to life!

You'll find extra Color and Play pages to encourage creativity. Color your favorite characters in different ways for hours of magical play!

A virtual version of specially marked coloring pages may also be purchased separately as an in-app purchase. If you have already purchased the virtual coloring pages, this book will not unlock any additional content.

Copyright © 2016 Disney/Pixar
All rights reserved.

The BENDON name, logo and Tear and Share are trademarks of Bendon, Inc., Ashland, OH 44805.

Apple, the Apple logo, and iPhone are trademarks of Apple Inc., registered in the U.S. and other countries. App Store is a service mark of Apple Inc. Google Play is a trademark of Google Inc.

Watch your picture come to life!

Hold your device over the picture until you see the  in the corners.

Hi, I'm Dory! Have we met before?

© Disney/Pixar

Watch your picture come to life!
Hold your device over the picture until you see the ☆ in the corners.

Hi, I'm Dory! Have we met before?

© Disney/Pixar

Watch your picture come to life!
Hold your device over the picture until you see the ⭐ in the corners.

Hi, I'm Dory! Have we met before?

© Disney/Pixar

Watch your picture come to life!
Hold your device over the picture until you see the ⭐ in the corners.

Hi, I'm Dory! Have we met before?

© Disney/Pixar

Watch your picture come to life!
Hold your device over the picture until you see the ⭐ in the corners.

Just keep swimming.

© Disney/Pixar

Watch your picture come to life!

Hold your device over the picture until you see the ☆ in the corners.

Just keep swimming.

© Disney/Pixar

© Disney/Pixar

Watch your picture come to life!
Hold your device over the picture until you see the ⭐☆⭐ in the corners.

Just keep swimming.

© Disney/Pixar

Watch your picture come to life!
Hold your device over the picture until you see the ☆ in the corners.

Just keep swimming.

© Disney/Pixar

Watch your picture come to life!
Hold your device over the picture until you see the ⭐☆⭐ in the corners.

Disney · PIXAR
FINDING DORY

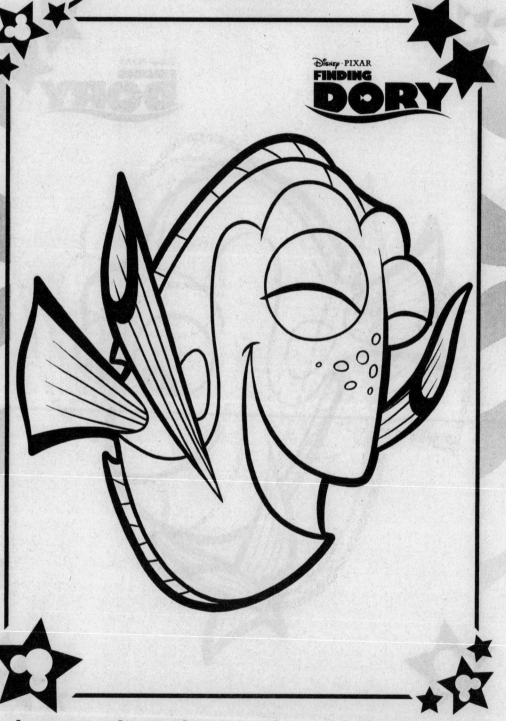

I remembered something! I think. . .

© Disney/Pixar

Watch your picture come to life!

Hold your device over the picture until you see the in the corners.

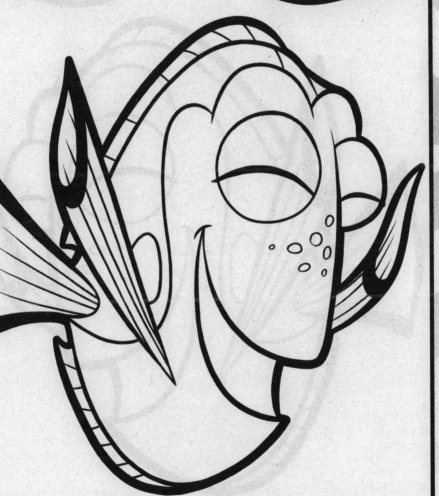

I remembered something! I think. . .

© Disney/Pixar

© Disney/Pixar

Watch your picture come to life!
Hold your device over the picture until you see the ⭐☆⭐ in the corners.

I remembered something! I think. . .

Watch your picture come to life!
Hold your device over the picture until you
see the ⭐ in the corners.

I remembered something! I think. . .

© Disney/Pixar

Watch your picture come to life!
Hold your device over the picture until you see the ⭐ in the corners.

Disney • PIXAR
FINDING DORY

What was I talking about?

© Disney/Pixar

Watch your picture come to life!
Hold your device over the picture until you
see the ⭐☆⭐ in the corners.

What was I talking about?

© Disney/Pixar

© Disney

Watch your picture come to life!
Hold your device over the picture until you see the ⭐☆⭐ in the corners.

Disney · PIXAR
FINDING DORY

What was I talking about?

© Disney/Pixar

Watch your picture come to life!
Hold your device over the picture until you see the ✩☆✩ in the corners.

© Disney/Pixar

DISNEY · PIXAR
FINDING DORY

What was I talking about?

© Disney/Pixar

Draw a picture!
Hold your device over the picture until you see the 🧩 in the corners to make a puzzle.

© Disney/Pixar

© Disney/Pixar

Disney
Color and **PLAY**
bendon

Draw a picture!
Hold your device over the picture until you see the 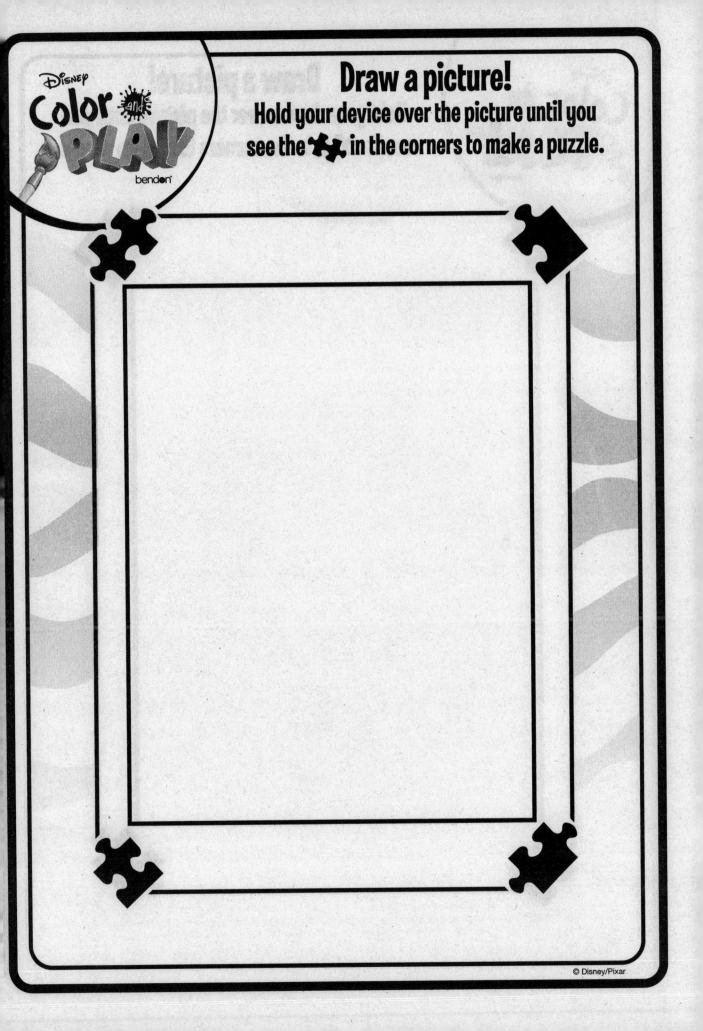 in the corners to make a puzzle.

© Disney/Pixar

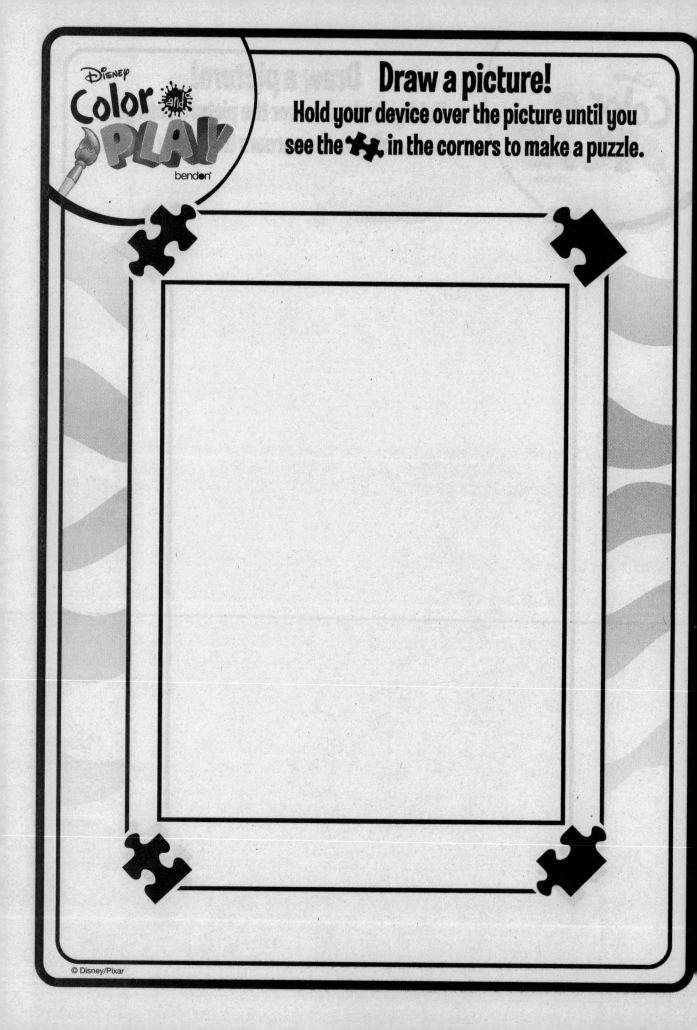

Draw a picture!

Hold your device over the picture until you see the 🧩 in the corners to make a puzzle.

© Disney/Pixar

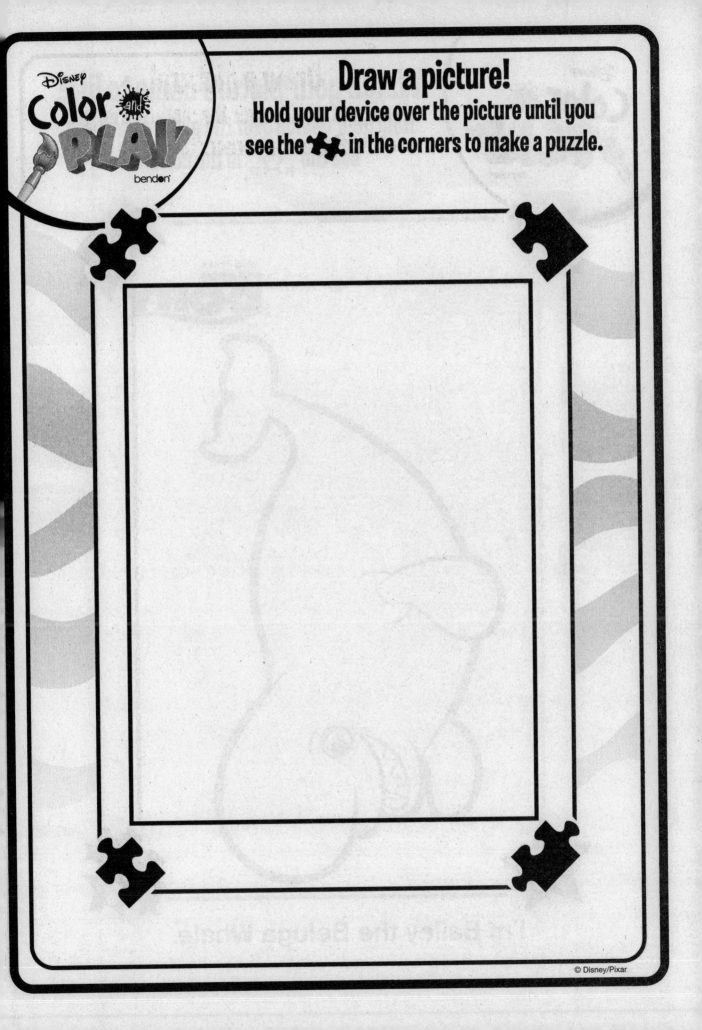

Disney
Color and **PLAY**
bendon

Draw a picture!
Hold your device over the picture until you
see the 🧩 in the corners to make a puzzle.

© Disney/Pixar

Disney
Color and **PLAY**
bendon

Watch your picture come to life!
Hold your device over the picture until you see the ☆ in the corners.

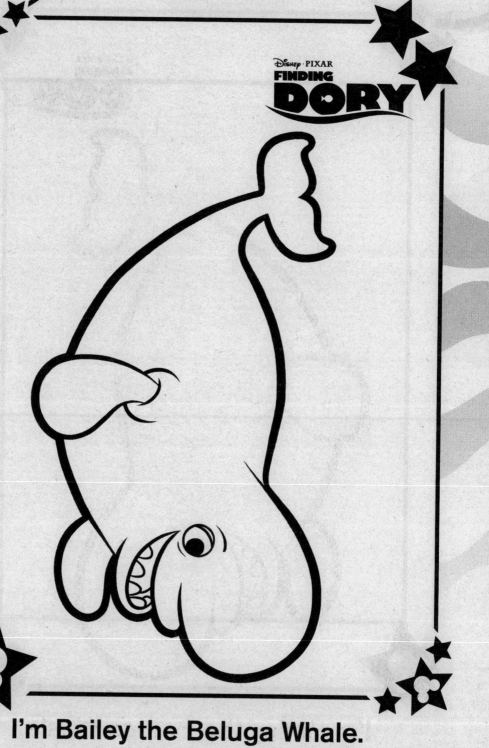

Disney·PIXAR
FINDING
DORY

I'm Bailey the Beluga Whale.

© Disney/Pixar

Disney
Color and PLAY
bendon

Watch your picture come to life!

Hold your device over the picture until you see the ☆ in the corners.

Disney·PIXAR
FINDING
DORY

I'm Bailey the Beluga Whale.

© Disney/Pixar

Watch your picture come to life!
Hold your device over the picture until you see the ⭐☆⭐ in the corners.

Disney·PIXAR
FINDING
DORY

I'm Bailey the Beluga Whale.

© Disney/Pixar

Watch your picture come to life!
Hold your device over the picture until you see the ⭐☆⭐ in the corners.

I'm Bailey the Beluga Whale.

© Disney/Pixar

Watch your picture come to life!
Hold your device over the picture until you see the ☆ in the corners.

Disney · PIXAR
FINDING DORY

I can see everything!

© Disney/Pixar

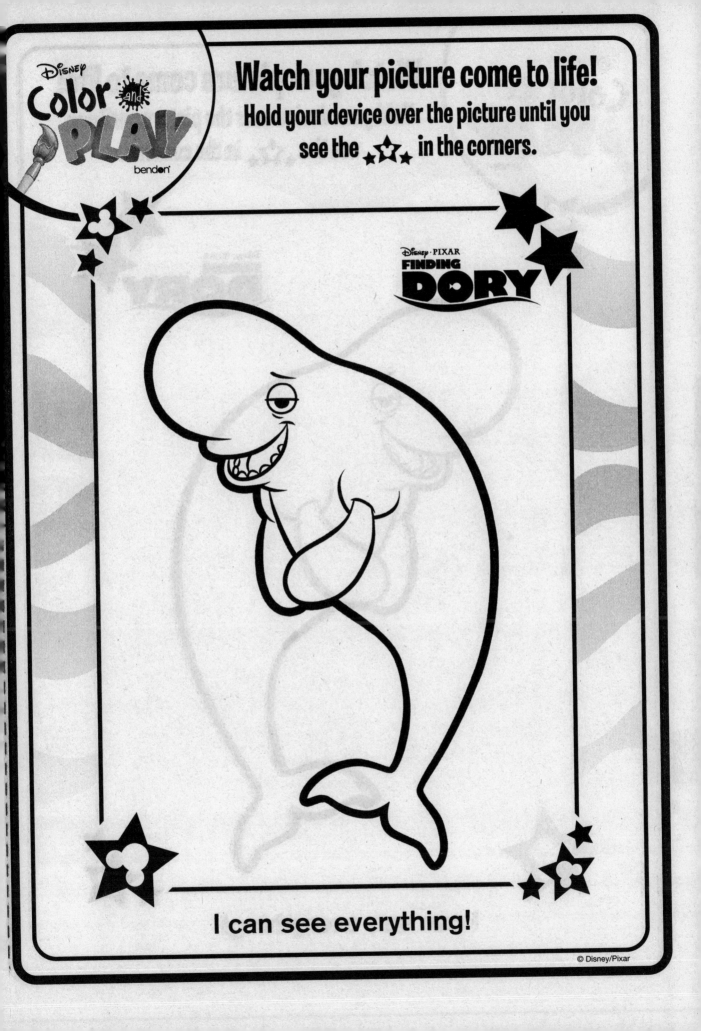

© Disney/Pixar

Watch your picture come to life!
Hold your device over the picture until you see the ☆☆ in the corners.

DISNEY · PIXAR
FINDING DORY

I can see everything!

© Disney/Pixar

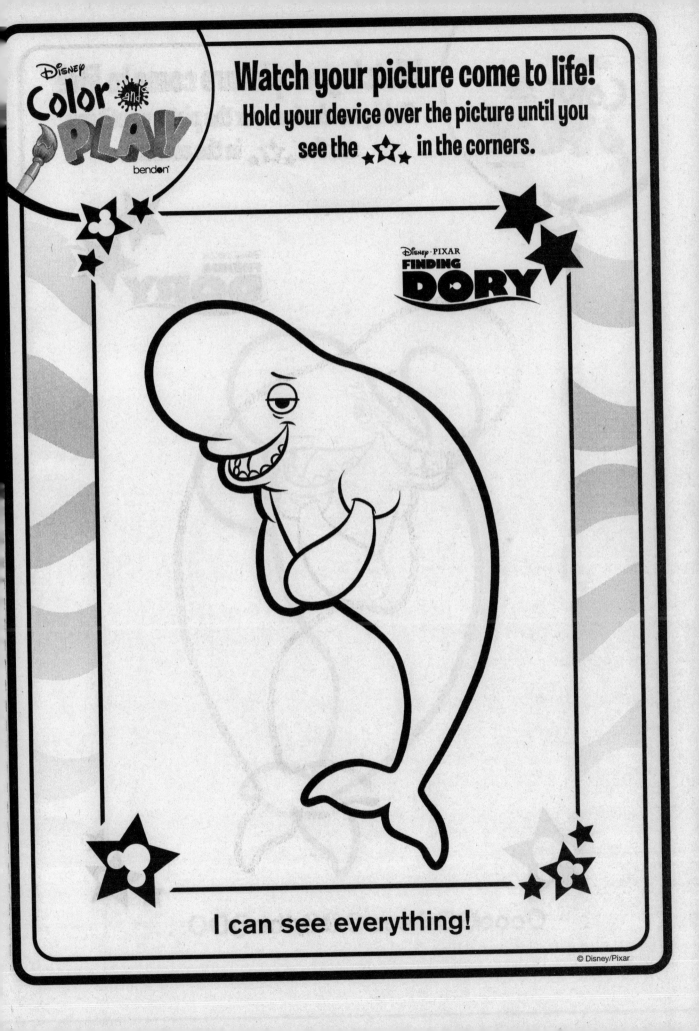

Watch your picture come to life!
Hold your device over the picture until you see the ★☆★ in the corners.

OooooOOOoooOOOoooOOO...

© Disney/Pixar

Watch your picture come to life!
Hold your device over the picture until you see the ⭐☆⭐ in the corners.

Ooooo000Oooo000Oooo000...

© Disney/Pixar

Watch your picture come to life!
Hold your device over the picture until you see the ☆ in the corners.

© Disney/Pixar

OooooOOOooooOOOooooOOO....

© Disney/Pixar

"Hi! I'm Dory. I suffer from short-term memory loss."

© Disney/Pixar

**Jenny and Charlie are Dory's parents.
They worry about her.**

© Disney/Pixar

Dory is lost. She asks other fish for help.

© Disney/Pixar

Dory has grown up.

© Disney/Pixar

Dory meets a fish named Marlin.
He's looking for his son, Nemo. Nemo is also lost!

© Disney/Pixar

Marlin is a clownfish. He is happy now that he has been reunited with his son.

© Disney/Pixar

Nemo lives with his dad in an anemone.

© Disney/Pixar

Marlin and Nemo enjoy living on the coral reef.

© Disney/Pixar

Marlin and Nemo are like family to Dory.

© Disney/Pixar

**Dory is Marlin and Nemo's neighbor.
She forgets that their anemone home can sting her.**

© Disney/Pixar

**Dory and Marlin swim to school with Nemo.
Marlin worries that Dory will get lost.**

© Disney/Pixar

Mr. Ray is Nemo's teacher.
He is also the school bus.

© Disney/Pixar

Here come the stingrays!

© Disney/Pixar

The hermit crabs live nearby.

© Disney/Pixar

Oh, no! They have awakened a scary giant squid!

© Disney/Pixar

Hank is also at the institute. He is an octopus with only seven arms. That makes him a septopus.

© Disney/Pixar

Destiny is a whale shark. Because of her poor eyesight, she cannot swim very well.

© Disney/Pixar

Dory helps her new friend swim on track.

© Disney/Pixar

Destiny excitedly speaks whale with Dory. They grew up together and would talk through the pipes.

© Disney/Pixar

Bailey is a beluga whale.
He thinks he hurt his head. If he were well, he could
use echolocation to detect things far away. © Disney/Pixar

Becky is a loon.
She can help Marlin and Nemo find Dory.

© Disney/Pixar

Marlin makes friends with Becky. She likes him!

© Disney/Pixar

Fluke and Rudder are sea lions.

© Disney/Pixar

Gerald is a sea lion. He is very playful.

© Disney/Pixar

Gerald gives his pail to Fluke and Rudder.

© Disney/Pixar

Becky loves popcorn.

© Disney/Pixar

Otters are cute and cuddly!

© Disney/Pixar

Dory and Hank are trapped in the touch pool!

© Disney/Pixar

Hank accidentally inks in the pool.

© Disney/Pixar

Dory remembers her parents teaching her the "Just Keep Swimming" song. She and Hank just need to keep swimming!

© Disney/Pixar

Dory and Hank make a great team!

© Disney/Pixar